The Dog that Belonged to No One

The Dog that Belonged to No One

Gerald A. Schiller

Illustrations by
Dawn Schiller

INTERCONTINENTAL PUBLISHING

ISBN 10881164-91-8
THE DOG THAT BELONGED TO NO ONE. An original
novel copyright © 1998 by Gerald A. Schiller.
Published by InterContinental Publishing. All rights
reserved.

Cover design: Dawn Schiller, Nightwatch Graphics
Author photo: John Torrey
Design and Typography: Sans Serif, Inc.

Author's Note

The story of Bum, the dog, is based on events that took place in the city of San Diego in the late 1800's. Many of the people and places referred to did exist, although I have made a number of changes and created many additional incidents.

Captain Friend was a real person and I have also utilized aspects of his life in the story, though here too I have enlarged upon and changed many events.

In my research it was often difficult to separate reality from fiction, so, in keeping with the many legends that have grown up about Bum, I have felt free to embellish on his amazing story.

My thanks for assistance in the research go to Dr. Eugene Chamberlin and to Sally West and the San Diego Historical Society, as well as all those who have written about Bum over the years and who have been impressed by his fascinating life.

1

The Fisherman

It had been a bad day for Ah Woe Sue. He sat in the bottom of his tiny fishing boat sorting his meager catch of the day. He knew even before he came into port that his catch was barely enough to sell for the few supplies he needed and food for him and his wife. Well, he thought, maybe tomorrow will be better. Maybe.

He filled the wooden buckets with his catch and stacked them neatly at one end of the boat. Then he started to clean up the deck, dipping an empty bucket into the water and soaking everything down thoroughly. Then he washed his knives. Ah Woe Sue always made sure everything on his tiny craft was clean before he left it. He liked to be able to start a new day fresh.

It was late in the afternoon and on shore he could

see the tradesmen in their wagons moving along "H" Street. The horses' hooves clop-clopped on the cobblestones, and the wagon wheels creaked under the weight of the loads. San Diego was a young city but it was alive with activity. Ah Woe Sue was glad he lived here—even though there were often bad fishing days like this one.

Suddenly there was a shrill blast of sound. It was a sound that he knew too well: the steamship whistle—the signal that a boat was arriving. He vividly remembered the day he had arrived in the city over ten years ago. He had stood on the steamer deck with all the other passengers, some fearful of this new place, others—like him—with a sense of excitement. He had not known what to expect, but he had felt a thrill that day, watching the activity on the shore as the steamer moved closer and closer.

That had been ten years ago. Ten years of exhausting labor as he struggled to make a living, going out each day in his boat to catch fish to sell. It was hard work, but he never really thought of it as hard. He made an honest living and he and his wife had a place to live and food on the table. What more could he ask for?

The whistle blasted again as the steamer moved up the channel into port. He never tired of watching these huge boats approach, their decks overflowing with people, their hulls full of cargo.

Now he could see the name lettered on the bow:

the *Santa Rosa*. He remembered it was the same ship that had brought him from San Francisco. The decks were crowded with eager passengers. He watched the activity: those on deck waving excitedly to those on shore who waited for them. Black smoke belched out of the smokestacks, and then there was another blast of the whistle.

In just a few minutes the *Santa Rosa* had reached the dock at the foot of Fifth Street and the crew had thrown the lines to the men below. In only a few more minutes the gangplank was down and a stream of passengers moved to the dock.

Soon there was the hustle and bustle of activity as the cargo was unloaded. Crates and barrels of food and merchandise were lugged to waiting wagons. A long line of wagons stood at the dock, ready to receive the goods. The horses snorted and stamped their hooves, impatient to be on their way.

As Ah Woe Sue watched the unloading—activity he had watched so many times before—this time he saw something different. It happened in almost an instant. As some huge barrels were being rolled down to the dock, there was a sudden flash of black and white that passed the busy workmen, sweating as they toiled.

Ah Woe Sue's eyes followed that flash of black and white as it reached the shore and he realized it was a dog. The dog had left the ship almost before anyone noticed and now stood watching the activity around it. The animal eagerly took in the sights and sounds of the busy dock, his tail wagging excitedly.

No one else seemed to notice the dog that had just come ashore. The workers were too busy loading cargo onto the waiting wagons, and the arriving passengers were being eagerly welcomed by those who had been waiting for them. There were hugs and kisses for loved ones and much excited conversation.

Ah Woe Sue watched the dog carefully. He moved among the people on the dock with curiosity, but not with fear, sniffing and exploring the new surroundings.

It occurred to the fisherman that this was not a dog that belonged to one of the passengers. It had no collar and no one seemed interested in it. This animal must have been a stowaway on the steamer. Somehow this dog had avoided discovery all the way from San Francisco to San Diego. And now he had come ashore.

This was a dog that belonged to no one. Here was a free spirit that had made a choice to leave his home and embark on a long and unknown journey. As he watched, the dog, unaware of his stare, walked warily among the busy passengers.

One or two of those standing at the dock patted the animal on the head, but when the black and white mongrel realized he was not going to get any handouts, he quickly sauntered off to look for more favorable possibilities.

The Dog that Belonged to No One

A nearby wagon was being loaded with some sides of beef. The dog immediately sniffed and saw a possible meal. Without a moment's hesitation, he jumped up on the back of the wagon, eagerly anticipating a delicious supper.

But the animal had underestimated the speed of the wagon driver in protecting his precious cargo. With an angry yell, he swung a stick at this thief who was about to steal his livelihood, knocking the animal off the wagon.

Ah Woe Sue was surprised to see that the dog did not limp away from his attacker in fear. He stood his ground just a few feet from the rear of the wagon, eyeing the driver. This was indeed a tough animal, thought the fisherman. He watched as the driver moved toward the dog with stick held high as if to hit him again, but the canine merely backed away a few steps, his eyes riveted on the man in front of him.

This was quite a fascinating situation, decided the fisherman.

But in a moment the stand-off ended as other men finished loading the wagon. The driver, after carefully making sure the dog was not going to attack his meat supply again, climbed up, shook the reins, and, with another look back at the dog, moved off.

Here was a spirited animal. He had lost the fight with the man but had kept his pride. Now the dog watched as the wagon rolled off toward Market Street.

The Fisherman

Ah Woe Sue looked at the animal. It was a rather dirty looking mongrel. He had the large head of a St. Bernard and the markings of a spaniel. The head and face were mostly black and there was an occasional black spot on the body. But most of the animal's fur was a dirty gray color.

The fisherman doubted if this dog had ever had a decent bath. He guessed from his size and friskiness that he was probably little more than a puppy— maybe a year or so old. From his behavior he also guessed that this was an animal used to living by his wits. He had never been spoiled by some kindly owner who put out tasty food regularly and romped with him in the park. This dog had never slept quietly by a warm fire at the feet of his loving protector. This was a dog of the streets.

Ah Woe Sue was curious. How would this dog respond to some kindness? He climbed out of his boat and began to move to where the animal stood. Would the dog be wary of him, now that his previous contact with a human had resulted in the smack of a stick?

But when he was within thirty feet or so of the black and white mongrel, something across the street caught the dog's eye. Was it another opportunity for a meal?

Ah Woe Sue never found out. In an instant, the dog had taken off at a run.

Well, he thought, so much for that. It will be interesting if I ever encounter that dog again, but it doesn't matter. I have fish to sell.

Although he didn't know it at the time, this would not be the fisherman's last meeting with the wary canine. It was only the beginning.

2

The City

In the year 1886, San Diego was a city of almost 12,000 people. It was also a growing city. Steamships, like the *Santa Rosa*, arrived twice each week bringing new and eager passengers. The California Southern Railway had recently extended its track to the city and more and more people arrived regularly at the train depot. Railroad fares had been reduced to a mere twenty-five dollars for a trip all the way from St. Louis, and each arrival of the train brought many new families to the city. These people had heard about the California sunshine and comfortable temperatures—almost all year round. They had also heard about the large amount of inexpensive land. Acres and acres of it. Why, anyone with a few hundred dollars could buy a parcel of land to farm, and California was eager to have its land settled.

Other new settlers were coming daily by wagon and stagecoach, making the long trek and arriving in the city dusty and dirty and tired. The city was growing so rapidly that there were hardly enough hotels and living spaces for the thousands of new arrivals. Granger's Corral provided a temporary camp for those who had come in wagons. It was somewhere for them to stay until they could find more permanent places to live.

Some of the new settlers wanted to start businesses. There were great opportunities for those with skills and good business sense to open a bakery or a shoemaker's shop or a feed store or any of a hundred more possibilities.

There were the less respectable businesses as well. There were saloons that attracted those with a thirst. Those poor souls often staggered home after spending their money on "demon rum."

There were also gambling dens where many would go to wager their few dollars on a throw of the dice or a poker game. Most of these people, however, would discover they came home much poorer than they arrived.

Now the dog trotted eagerly along the dusty streets, taking in the bustle of activity. Delivery wagons moved along, carrying their goods. Several carriages passed with people on their way home or off on a visit. Newsboys hawked their papers on the street corners and street vendors tried to attract customers to buy their wares.

The dog soon saw there was not much chance of a meal here on the busy streets. So he moved around behind the shops where he might find something edible. As he passed a restaurant, he noticed a man leaving the back door carrying something wrapped in paper. He could smell the scraps of meat and paused, watching the man deposit the leftover bits in a trash barrel. As soon as the man had gone back in, the dog carefully approached the barrel and sprang up, tipping it over. Quickly he found the delicious scraps.

Eagerly he gobbled the bits of meat—his first good meal in the last few days. But suddenly he heard a yell and looked up to see that the man had returned and was shouting at him. The animal backed away slowly, watching him. Then he saw the man pick up something from the ground, and sensing danger, turned and trotted off just as a stone whizzed by his head.

But there were other sources of food. Not far away the dog discovered the rear of a butcher shop, and this proved to be a good place for him to stop. As he sniffed around the back door, it suddenly opened and a large man, wearing an apron covered with red stains, noticed the pooch.

"Lookin' for a handout, I'll bet," said the man, wise and sympathetic to the ways of stray animals.

"Here's somethin' for ya."

And he tossed out some tasty cuttings which the dog eagerly devoured. Then he followed this gift with a large meat bone. The dog greedily grabbed the bone in its teeth and began to gnaw on it.

"Now don't expect me to feed ya all the time. You're gonna have to find some other poor sap next time. Remember that."

He was pointing at the dog.

"Now take that bone and get out a' here. Git on now."

The dog understood the man's hospitality was over, but he was grateful for the kindness. He looked up at the generous man, then turned, and, bone still clenched in his jaws, trotted off.

Now that his stomach was satisfied, the dog continued his exploration of the city. There was indeed much to see.

He passed the camp where there were wagons loaded with the possessions of those who had recently arrived. Men and women could be seen setting up temporary places to live, putting up tents, and preparing to cook their dinners. Children ran about, shouting and playing.

He continued exploring and soon reached the railroad depot. This was a new experience for the animal. As he trotted past the train tracks, he suddenly became aware of a shrill whistle screaming behind him, and, as he turned, he could see the huge locomotive chugging along the tracks.

The City

The dog was wise enough to move away from this frightening sight. But he watched with interest—from a distance—as the huge train pulled up to the station and the eager new arrivals climbed down, carrying their luggage and packages.

From there he moved to the town plaza, following a group of children who were running excitedly drawn to the sound of a loud brass band. The dog watched as people gathered around the bandstand. He could see the musicians in their gaudy jackets and the leader swinging his baton as they played. Then the music stopped, and the people in the crowd clapped their hands enthusiastically.

As the dog watched all this activity, he was aware of someone standing beside him. It was a boy of about eight looking down at him. The boy put out his hand and gently petted the dog.

"Hello. Do you have a name, doggie?"

The dog looked up at him.

"I bet you don't have a home, do you?"

The child ran his hands over the dog's back and scratched him behind the ears. It felt good.

"You like that, huh?"

Suddenly there was the voice of a woman behind them.

"Lucius! What are you doing?"

She pulled the boy away from the dog.

"Don't touch that dirty animal. Come along now, we've got to get home."

The boy turned and looked back at the dog, but the woman was tugging at his arm, and he was pulled away down the street.

The dog stayed for some time as the band concert continued. Then it was time to find some place to sleep. He trotted off to find a spot where he wouldn't be chased. It had been a very busy day.

3

The Newsboys

The dog awoke in the chill of the early morning. A light fog had settled on the city. He had found a spot out of the cold behind a small shack not far from the bandstand. He rose and shook himself and yawned. He moved around the small building just as a wagon pulled up with a sleepy driver and an old horse that seemed to be following a route he had been repeating day in and day out for a long time. The old driver climbed down wearily and began to unload stacks of newspapers bound together with string, piling them up in front of the shack. The dog watched from a distance.

By the time the papers had all been stacked, the animal could hear the shouts of youngsters approaching. He turned to see a group of boys approaching the shack, playfully running and leaping and joking with each other as they moved through the early morning fog.

Each was about ten or eleven years old and all were dressed in clothing that didn't seem to fit: hand-me-downs from some older child. One wore baggy coveralls and a large woolen sweater. Most of the others wore woolen jackets, knickers and long, sagging socks. They had all dressed in a hurry to get here, pulling themselves out of bed at this early hour.

The dog watched as each boy picked up a load of papers, threw the load up on his shoulders and moved off down the street, each in a different direction.

As usual the animal was curious. He decided to follow one of the boys, and, keeping a respectful distance behind him, trotted along as the boy struggled under his heavy load.

Just a short walk from where he had picked up the papers, he saw the boy dump his load down on the sidewalk in front of a bakery shop, undo the string, then pick up two copies and hold them up to show to those passing on foot or riding by in wagons or carriages.

It was still early and not many people were out yet, but several tradesmen in wagons pulled up to where the boy stood, handed him some coins, and took one of the papers.

As the boy turned to see if anyone was coming behind him, he noticed the dog for the first time. He moved to where the dog stood and put out his hand, keeping the papers tucked under his other arm.

"Hello, poochie. Have you been followin' me?"

He patted the dog gently on the head and began to stroke his back.

"You sure don't have a collar, do you. Are you lost?"

He continued stroking the animal's fur and noticed how dirty and matted it was.

"You're a stray, ain't you? But I've never seen ya around here before. You must've wandered over from some other part a' town, huh? Well, I'm sure you're hungry. Maybe I can find some food for ya if ya stay for awhile."

The dog was enjoying the attention and the gentle touches, but suddenly the boy pulled away to stop a man who was moving by and wanted to buy a paper. He made the sale, then moved back to the dog.

"I'll bet ya don't have a home. And ya probably don't even have a name either."

"Hey, paper boy!"

A man on a wagon loaded with bags of feed had pulled up to buy his paper. The boy moved over and handed the newspaper up to him where he sat.

"That your dog?" asked the wagon driver.

"No, sir. He just followed me, I think."

"Well, if you want him, be sure he gets a bath. He's about the mangiest mongrel I've seen around here in

a long time. Giddap!" And the horse sauntered off down the dusty street.

There were several more sales to make. It had become a busy day, and when the boy turned around to see where the dog was, he was surprised to see the animal was gone. Just when he felt he had been deserted, he saw the dog scampering toward him eagerly clutching a bone in his teeth.

"Well, I'll be darned. You don't seem to need my help in bummin' some food—or maybe stealin' it. Hey, there's a name I can call ya. Bum. You're just like a bum, with no home or owner. But ya sure can bum food if ya need it, I guess. Then I think I'll call you Bum."

So the dog got a name, a name that would stick to him all his life. He became Bum. It was definitely a most appropriate name for this animal. Bum, the vagrant. Bum, the freeloader. Bum, who would become the wandering dog of the city—everybody's dog— and nobody's dog. Bum, a free spirit. Bum, who would be envied by many, feared by a few, and loved by almost everyone who knew him.

But that is getting ahead of the story.

4

The Fight

O ver the next few days, Bum became the unofficial mascot of the paperboys of San Diego. He followed one or another of them, received lots of affection and frequent food scraps, explored the city, and in general began to feel a part of the life of the community.

One of the boys, Tommy Maxwell, decided he wanted to adopt the dog and take him home. Bum dutifully followed Tommy and enjoyed, for a time, becoming part of the boy's household. But when Tommy and his father decided to give the dog a bath, that proved to be the end of the relationship. Bum was scrubbed (with a bit of a fight) and ended up with a very clean, shiny coat. But it was an experience the dog did not intend to repeat—despite the saying "cleanliness is next to Godliness." Apparently Bum had no plans to be religious.

The next day when Tommy took him to pick up his papers, the fickle animal trotted off with Willy Sanders.

After a short time, the boys agreed that Bum preferred an independent way of life. He liked his freedom, and, while he might occasionally spend a night or two at the home of one of the paperboys, he would not stay longer. No one could really be his owner. He was a dog that belonged to no one.

Soon Bum began to be recognized by others around town as well. Tradesmen would give him a friendly pat, handouts from butcher shops became more frequent. He was becoming the town dog.

There were, of course, other dogs in San Diego and some of them were highly protective of their own turf. One was a tough bulldog owned by Matt Morris. Morris ran the saloon that was at the far end of town, just across from the railroad tracks. He called his dog "Diablo," which means "devil" in Spanish. And it was a most appropriate name.

Over the years, Diablo had had several vicious fights with other dogs that had tried to take over his territory. He had been responsible for quite a few torn ears and deep gashes. He had even caused the partial blindness of one poor animal who had made the mistake of getting too close to Diablo's territory. The bulldog also bore the scars of many of those encounters as well. But he had always been the winner. Few

The Fight

dogs who had fought with him once had the nerve to get close to this fierce champion a second time.

Bum was not much of a fighter. He had not been involved in more than one or two fights in his entire life, but he had one characteristic that perhaps was just as strong as a fighting spirit. He was independent and totally single-minded. In his brief life he had developed an intense will to survive.

One day a few weeks after he had arrived in the city, Bum was happily following Willy Sanders, one of the paperboys, as he found a good spot to peddle his wares. It just so happened that the spot he chose was just outside Matt Morris' saloon, the saloon that stood across from the railroad tracks—the saloon that was Diablo's home territory. Bum, as he often did, was sniffing around the area and noticed those quaint and curious swinging doors that—in those days—symbolized the place where (in the words of the song):

The doors swing in and the doors swing out;
Some pass in and many pass out.

As he stuck his head under the doors, Bum came face to face with the fearsome bulldog. Diablo was not a dog to begin an encounter graciously. His approach was a simple one: a growl, a bark, and an attack.

Before he knew what had happened, Bum found

himself rolling in the dirt outside the saloon with the vicious bulldog's teeth sunk in his ear, struggling for all he was worth just to get free.

But Diablo was not one just to issue a warning. When Bum had broken free, the bulldog attacked again. Soon it was a vicious struggle with Bum fighting just to defend himself and Diablo fighting for conquest.

The noise had attracted a crowd—especially those in the saloon. They always enjoyed the spectacle of Diablo making mincemeat of any stray who might blunder by. The bar patrons filed out, glasses in hand, cheering on the champion of the drinking crowd.

Willy, the terrified newsboy, at first tried to stop the fight, but soon realized this would be impossible. He stood by helplessly as the violent struggle continued.

Again Bum was able to pull himself free of the angry attacker, but Diablo struck still a third time. Bum was still outclassed but this time he had learned from the first assaults and sank his own teeth into Diablo's ear, causing the bulldog to wince in pain and then to renew his vicious biting into Bum's flesh.

Neither dog knew it but as they rolled and chewed at each other in the dirt, the train from Los Angeles was making its way down the tracks into their city. The engineer was totally unaware that just as he applied his brakes to slow the huge steel monster, two angry canines were about to roll onto the tracks, ig-

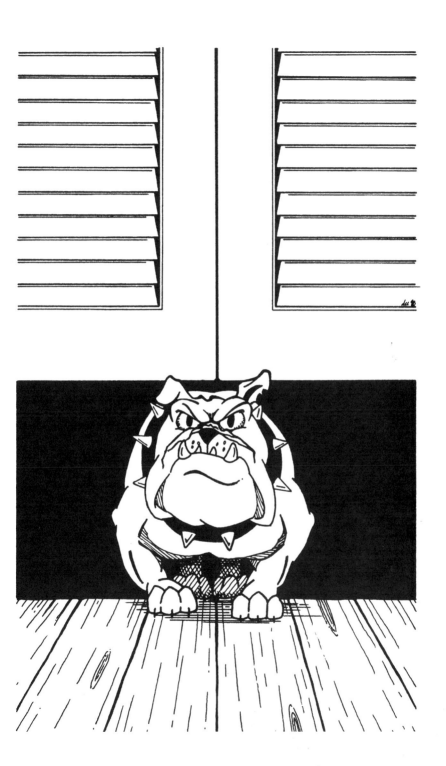

noring the steam and noise of his locomotive as it pulled into the station.

The paperboy saw what was about to happen as did the saloon gawkers, but with the dust billowing and the steam screaming from the train, no one knew what to do.

Then, over the noise of the locomotive, they heard the whine of the dogs. By now the train had stopped and everyone rushed to where they had last seen the two animals struggling.

Through the dust limped the bruised and battered figure of Bum, spattered with blood. Diablo, however, did not emerge. The crowd found only the mutilated body of the bulldog. He had fought his last fight.

Diablo was dead. But Bum was not in very good shape either. Willy knelt down to comfort the battered dog, not knowing what to do.

The animal's right forepaw was badly crushed, some of his tail had been torn off, and there was blood all over his belly. He was exhausted and barely able to walk. Then Willy heard a voice behind him and turned to see a Chinese fisherman standing nearby, watching the dog.

"This dog need help," said the fisherman.

It was Ah Woe Sue, the man who many days ago had seen Bum leave the ship, and had occasionally noticed him as he followed the newsboys on their travels through the city.

The Fight

He leaned over and picked up the weakened animal in his strong arms.

"I take him home. He need help or he die."

So Ah Woe Sue carried Bum to his tiny home on the outskirts of the city. The fisherman and his wife bathed the wounds and fed the dog for several days. Using some herbs he bought from one of his knowing countrymen and a strong broth, Ah Woe Sue helped Bum regain his strength. The fisherman's medicine and care and Bum's overwhelming spirit of survival combined to help the animal slowly return to health. After several weeks he seemed to be himself again.

But there were two very real scars of the fight. Bum's tail was much shorter—it was now just a few inches long. And his right front paw was now little more than a stump. He would become known as the dog who limped on just three legs, an appearance that would make him a well-recognized figure throughout the town.

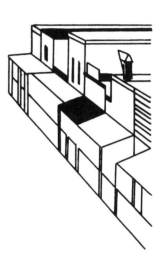

5

The Fire Wagon

Soon Bum's wounds had healed and he was able to limp around. He seemed not too restricted by a missing paw, and, with his usual independence, soon made a quick departure from Ah Woe Sue's home. The fisherman knew it would happen. He had helped Bum recover and expected nothing in return. He had sensed from the first time he saw the dog that he had a strong sense of freedom. So one morning when the fisherman awoke, he was not surprised to discover that Bum was gone.

"I help him and now he go off on his own," he thought, and he moved down the road to the dock, hoping for a good fishing day.

Bum had been well fed by Ah Woe Sue, but food alone was not enough to keep him in one place. Besides, he was a city dog and there were plenty of handouts available out there from those who knew him.

Soon he was spotted by two newsboys as he limped with his new three-legged walk. Bum immediately became the center of attention. The boys crouched down beside him and were lavish with their petting and stroking. Bum, of course, relished the attention. He was about to follow them as he had done so many times before his accident, when suddenly he heard a loud clanging from down the street. The boys leaped up and ran to see what was happening.

Down the street at a gallop came two horses pulling the town's fire wagon. The wagon clanged its bell and zoomed along the street with the three firemen on board just about hanging on for dear life.

Bum was eager to become part of all the excitement. Unaware of what it was or where it was going, Bum took off with his three-legged run to follow the wagon as it clanged along the dusty street.

Soon the driver pulled his team to a halt in front of a tiny house with smoke pouring out of its windows. The firemen leaped down, started pumping the water from the wagon and soon had the fire under control.

Bum watched the smoldering structure with wide eyes. This was indeed a new experience. One of the firemen noticed the dog and came over to pet him.

"It's that dog Bum," said the man who had recog-

nized the dog and, like quite a few in the town, had heard the story of Bum's struggle with Diablo.

"Come on up, Bum," called the wagon driver, and Bum, who rarely refused an interesting invitation, hopped up on the fire wagon.

So Bum had a new career. But since there were fires to go to only now and then, he divided his time between accompanying the newsboys, as he had done before, and becoming Bum, the fire dog.

Whenever the alarm sounded and the wagon with its horses could be heard rattling down the street, Bum would take off after it, rushing alongside the firemen and enjoying all the excitement.

Often Bum could be found at the Number One Fire Station on Third Street where the firemen appreciated his company and happily shared their meals with him.

This was one more of the many adventures the dog would experience. For Bum was truly becoming San Diego's town dog.

6

The Captain

Late in the fall of 1886, with Bum firmly established in his regular activities both as newsboys' dog and firemen's dog, a stagecoach pulled into town, creaking to a stop at the Wells Fargo office at the corner of Sixth and "H" Streets.

There was only one passenger on board. The man climbed down from the stage and tried to shake off the dust that covered his clothing after the many miles he had traveled from San Bernardino.

The man stretched and rubbed his sore body. After the rough and bouncing ride he had endured on the bone-jarring coach, he was happy to have finally arrived at his destination.

He seemed well-dressed although a closer inspection of his clothing might show it was really quite threadbare. He was tall and thin, had long wavy dark hair and a mustache, and seemed to have a constant smile on his face—as if the long, tiring trip had had no effect on his attitude about the world.

The driver handed him the one carpet bag that was his only luggage. He graciously thanked the two men who had helped get him to San Diego. Then, after getting directions, he walked the six short blocks to the Horton House Hotel.

The man stopped at the hotel desk, turned the large registration ledger around, and in elegant hand-writing, signed his name with a flourish. He withdrew a silver dollar from his pocket, placed it neatly on the counter and took the key the hotel clerk handed him. He picked up his dusty carpet bag, thanked the clerk, and headed up the stairs to his room.

As the hotel clerk, and soon many others in the town discovered, his name was James E. Friend— Captain James E. Friend.

He had earned that rank as a member of the defeated Confederate Army some twenty-three years before in the Civil War. At the tender age of twenty-four, James Friend had commanded a troop of eager young men at the battle of Vicksburg.

After Lee's defeat and the end of the war, Captain Friend had returned to his native Alabama, and worked for a local printer, then at the Wells Fargo telegraph office. He was also an aspiring writer, and wrote an occasional article for the local paper.

The Captain

However, a series of misfortunes had had a shattering effect on his life. He had picked up a chronic cough in the army (sleeping outside in every kind of weather). The cough had flared up and forced him to miss many days of work. His employers, though sympathetic, had to dismiss him, and, to compound his suffering, his wife of but one year, Letitia, had suddenly taken ill and died of smallpox.

Depressed by these misfortunes, Captain Friend had decided to leave his native state and head west, where the weather (he was told) was much better, and where many opportunites (he was also told) existed for those who were eager to expand their horizons.

Though Captain Friend was not aware of it yet, his future would become closely involved with that of the dog Bum. These two independent individuals would shortly discover they had many things in common.

Fate had brought the two of them to San Diego and that same fate would soon bring them together in an unusual partnership that would last for many years.

7

The Writer

Having survived both fight and accident—helped of course by the kindly fisherman—Bum returned to his daily activities. He continued to follow one or another of the newsboys each morning and keep them company. The paperboys would usually provide him with some food as pay for his company. Later in the day, he made the rounds of the restaurants and shops that recognized him. There always seemed to be someone to provide some scraps or a bone to gnaw on.

Often when the fire wagon rattled along the streets on its way to a fire, Bum dashed alongside it, or leaped up beside the driver to ride in style as the wagon dashed to help put out some blaze that had gotten out of control.

The Dog that Belonged to No One

Captain Friend spent his first days in the city doing what most new arrivals do: looking for work.

The telegraph office had no openings. The two printing shops in town already had several master printers and numerous young, sweating apprentices working hard to learn the printing trade. These rejections did not, however, disturb the Captain. He continued his search with a smile on his face and a jaunty walk as he moved through the town.

When he noticed the office of *The San Diego Union,* a popular newspaper of the town, he felt that—if he was lucky—this might provide the answer to his need for work.

At this time *The Union* was one of two newpapers San Diegans could purchase. This was the paper of Old Town—started eighteen years before Captain Friend had arrived. Its rival was *The Sun,* the paper of "New Town"—supported by Alonzo Horton, whose hotel was where Captain Friend was now spending his evenings.

Captain Friend carried with him clippings from an Alabama newspaper to which he had made a few contributions. Fortunately he had arrived on the very day that two of *The Union's* reporters had just left— lured away by offers of higher salaries from the rival *Sun.*

In short order James Friend found himself employed to report on local events by a desperate editor.

But he was hired on a trial basis. He had to produce stories that would help sell papers.

Captain Friend was overjoyed with his success. Even though his writing experience had been limited, here he was on the second day in his newly adopted city, hired to report for *The Union*.

He stood outside the newspaper office, smiling his perpetual smile, curling his mustache, and surveying his newly adopted town.

And that was the moment he first saw Bum.

Along the street, with his familiar three-legged canter, bounded Bum at the heels of one of the newsboys. The boy carried the few papers that remained from his morning sales.

Captain Friend watched as the dog quickly received the attention of all the boys gathered around the building. The captain moved to where the youngsters surrounded the dog and watched the activity for a few moments. Then, in his most gracious and elegant style he introduced himself.

"Good day, everyone."

The boys suddenly noticed this stranger and stopped to look at him. Bum also looked up.

"May I introduce myself? My name is Captain James Friend, just newly arrived in this fair city. Starting tomorrow I shall be reporting for your employer, *The San Diego Union*. So you may be seeing a good deal of me around here for awhile."

Bum gave a bark.

"Well, hello, to you too. And who is the owner of this rather unusual canine?"

Tommy Maxwell was first to speak.

"Nobody owns that dog, mister. That's Bum. He's kinda the town dog. He goes pretty much where he wants, when he wants to. Most of the time he follows us paperboys around."

"Or else he chases the fire wagon," chimed in Eli Malloy.

Captain Friend was impressed. He moved to Bum, crouched down and began to pet him.

"Hello, Bum. Nice to meet you."

Bum looked up at this new provider of affection and let out a happy bark. It was as if, at this very first meeting, Bum recognized a kindred spirit in this smiling man.

Perhaps Captain Friend recognized that this solitary creature lived by his wits, much like him; survived on a meager existence, again like him; and enjoyed each day as it arrived—which had always been the Captain's outlook on life.

As the two faced each other, there seemed to be an instant attraction. And though neither knew it at the time, the lives of these two were soon to become closely intertwined.

Captain Friend looked around at the group, thought about his new good fortune in finding employment, and felt generous.

"Young gentlemen, since you all seem to be fin-

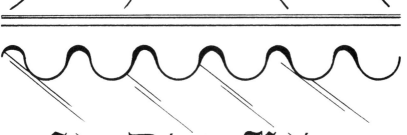

San Diego Union
ESTABLISHED 1868

ished with your day's work, how about joining me for some sweets—the treat will be on me!"

The boys let out a cheer and Eli shouted, "This way—to Vogel's Emporium."

The group was led by Eli, followed closely by the other four boys; next came Captain Friend, with Bum bringing up the rear. They proceeded across the street to Vogel's Emporium and General Store.

There the generous Captain purchased (at the grandiose sum of a penny each) sweets for all the boys—as well as for himself—and the group sat in front of Vogel's savoring the captain's generous gifts.

"Was you in the war?" inquired the curious Tommy Maxwell of their new friend.

"Yes, indeed," replied the captain.

"Which side was you on?"

There was a moment of hesitation.

Captain Friend knew that even in places like California, where veterans of both sides of the War Between the States were represented, there were still remnants of anger and hatred. Sympathy for both North and South was still strong. But these were young boys, born perhaps fifteen years after the conflict, so he decided to answer their questions directly and honestly.

"I served in General Lee's Army. I wore the gray uniform of the South."

There was a pause.

The Writer

Then Marcus Burns—with some awe in his voice—blurted out, "You was—a rebel!"

"Yes, indeed. I fought for the side that lost. But it's all over now—all over and behind us," sighed the Captain.

Tommy, the inquisitive one, had to know more. "Did yuh see folks die?"

The Captain closed his eyes, now with an audience that showed rapt attention, and his thoughts went back to the screams and the violence of the battlefield.

"Yes—too many."

"Tell us," insisted Tommy.

The Captain opened his eyes and looked around at the eager faces. Even Bum was watching him.

"Another time, my friends. Another time. For now I must be on my way, but we will meet again. Perhaps then I will relate some of my war experiences."

Captain Friend rose and started back to the Horton House Hotel as the boys and the dog followed at a respectful distance, soon moving off to go their own separate ways. The youngsters had much to look forward to now as this new and interesting person promised to relate exciting—and maybe even bloody—tales. It looked to be a fascinating prospect for the future.

8

The Reporter

Captain Friend began his duties as reporter for *The San Diego Union* with a seriousness and eagerness that surprised many on the newspaper's staff. Even though he was given assignments no one else would take, he carried through with efficiency and a constant smile on his face.

He visited the police station and reported on every minor offender who was dragged in by the authorities. Soon the cops all knew him and kept him informed of what was happening in each part of town.

He followed the fire wagon—when he could—and, like Bum, soon knew the firemen. His reports on each blaze were brief and kept to the facts—and they usually could be found tucked away on the paper's last page.

The captain followed orders and did the jobs the

editor assigned him without complaint. After all, he was a full-fledged reporter now and had joined the ranks of those distinguished members of the *Union's* experienced staff.

He moved to a room at a boarding house on Seventh Street where he was provided with a place to sleep, dinner each night, and the company of the other boarders—all at five dollars per month. Captain Friend felt he had taken a giant step in his life. Fate, or perhaps some divine presence, had been good to him.

The captain did not forget the boys he had met that first day either. Regularly each payday he took them to Vogel's Emporium for sweets and once each month he met with them on a Sunday afternoon for a fun-filled day at City Park.

There he organized relay races and joined with them in games like blindman's bluff. He made sure that each boy had his mother prepare a contribution of food for everyone to share.

After the games he would often tell stories of his war experiences, though making sure to withhold the most violent and grisly details.

He soon became the newsboys' friend.

Bum, during this time, continued his pleasant life as town dog. The newsboys and local storekeepers kept him well fed. He followed his regular ritual each day accompanying one of the paperboys. When there was a fire, Bum could always be found riding the firewagon, his bark announcing the arrival of help for those in need.

But Bum was not one to fall into habits that prevented him from seeking other new experiences. He often embarked on some challenging exploration that might cause his absence for a day or even more. Though the paperboys would often wonder where he was, they knew he would eventually be back.

Bum was curious and eager to explore and find out more about his surroundings. Since many people in the town knew him, he was frequently recognized on his explorations and tended to get away with a lot that other dogs would never have been permitted to do.

One day Bum decided to board a train for Los Angeles. He boldly climbed up on the train along with the other—two-legged— passengers. At first the conductor tried to move the dog to the baggage car, where animals were supposed to be kept. But Bum vigorously protested, and when another passenger explained who this famous dog was, once again the rules were set aside. Throughout the trip Bum sat proudly on a coach seat watching the passing scenery through the window.

Captain Friend had seen him board the train and had the telegraph operator send a dispatch to the Los Angeles station which said:

"Bum, San Diego's town dog is on board the train arriving in Los Angeles at 10:20 am. Should he decide to honor your city with a visit, please extend him the courtesy and keys thereof. Please also see to it that he has a good time and travels home on a pass."

Bum's reputation was already known in Los Angeles. When the message was received, the offices of the *Los Angeles Herald* were notified and reporter Dick Clover met the train, gave Bum a tour of the city, and had him back on the train to San Diego before the end of the day.

Bum had a pleasant journey, and the reporter ended up with a great story for the next day's paper.

Another of Bum's explorations was to Coronado.

In those days a ferry made the trip to that little community across San Diego Bay. Visitors would usually make the journey into a day's excursion.

One sunny morning Bum climbed casually on board the ferry along with the other passengers. Quite a few recognized him as the well-known paperboys' dog who was seen all over town.

Across the Bay was a tiny community inhabited by only a few families. In those days it was mostly empty space. Bum romped across the fields, found his way to the shore and splashed playfully in the surf.

What the dog was not aware of, however, was that on board the ferry he had ridden was a man who would—possibly—have the greatest influence on that area. His name was E. S. Babcock. He would later be responsible for building on this almost barren bit of land an attraction that would be known throughout the world.

When Mr. Babcock left the ferry, he spent his day exploring this area that most San Diegans called "The Peninsula." He climbed a rise and surveyed the beautiful coastline. As Bum frolicked in the surf not far from where he stood, Babcock's mind was thinking of the image of a huge hotel—a hotel that would resemble a Norman Castle, like those he had seen on his recent trip to France. It would be one of the grandest hotels in the world, he imagined, and it would attract presidents and kings and all those who wanted to enjoy the healthful air and the spectacular ocean views.

As the ferry returned to town late in the afternoon both Bum and Mr. Babcock were on it. And while Bum was looking forward to picking up some leftovers from a nearby restaurant, E.S. Babcock was making plans to raise the money to finance this major undertaking. In a relatively short time, his dream would become a reality. Within a year, ships would be bringing in the timber, a brickyard would be set up on the peninsula, and freight cars would arrive to supply the furniture for this grandest of hotels that— by 1888—would open to the public as the world famous Hotel del Coronado.

However, as Bum cantered—in his three-legged hop—down the gangplank of the ferry, who should notice him but Captain Friend.

"Well, what do you know!" said the Captain as the dog pranced over to him.

"I didn't know that dogs took day trips to the Peninsula when they felt like it. But, of course, you're certainly not just any dog. You're Bum, the town dog, and I guess that gives you privileges no other dog has. Come along, Bum, let's find you something for dinner. It's just a shame you can't tell me all about your experiences today. I'll wager it's been a fascinating day for you."

And Bum and Captain Friend headed down the street to find some dinner.

9

The Editor

Captain Friend worked diligently at *The Union* for seven months and kept up his friendship with the newsboys and Bum. Although he always had a pleasant smile as he worked on the assignments he was given, he began to feel that his talents needed additional opportunities.

He had saved a bit of money and had learned a great deal about the newspaper business. One evening as he sat alone in his room, he decided the time had come to make a move in his career. He was going to leave *The Union* to start his own paper. It would be a modest one at first, but he would be editor (and probably reporter as well) and he would present the city with a different approach to the news. There would be more stories about the ordinary people of the town, the folk who made their modest contributions to the life of the city. Let *The Union* cover the politicians and fires and criminals and habits of the famous and wealthy. His paper would celebrate the townspeople who had accomplished things that might seem minor, but who, he believed, definitely should be recognized.

Captain Friend decided to call his newspaper *The Weekly Drift*. He eagerly took out some paper and a pencil to lay out the plans for his project.

He lost no time getting organized. The very next day—between assignments—he stopped at Bruner's Print Shop to get information on what the printing costs would be. Then he found a tiny vacant store that would suit him admirably as the location for his new enterprise. He located some used furniture in a shop on Market Street: a desk, a table, and some chairs to furnish his new office. Then he sat down with his pencil and paper to figure out whether his modest finances could handle all this.

Satisfied that he could—with careful spending—finance the new project, Captain Friend decided to spend the remaining few dollars he would have left on a device for his new newspaper: a typewriter. He was able to find a battered one in a pawn shop and nursed it back to health with some tender loving care and the few mechanical skills he possessed. (The machine was, however, a constant problem and caused him no end of annoyance as long as he used it.)

With his plan now in full swing, the future editor

of *The Weekly Drift* approached his boss at *The Union* and gave his notice.

Two weeks from that day he would launch his new enterprise and, with a good deal of excitement, he began planning the scope and format of San Diego's newest newspaper.

10

The Drift

The first issue of *The Weekly Drift* was a mere four pages. It had a front page introducing the new tabloid to the readers, a biography of Captain Friend, the editor, and a few items the captain had taken with him from his regular rounds working for *The Union*.

Inside he included some advertisements he had secured from a few friends and acquaintances, information on weather and tides he had taken from his former paper, and some classified notices about items for sale, weddings, lost pets and other bits of information for his readership. It was not much of a first edition, but the captain felt like a proud parent showing off his new baby.

Eagerly he walked the San Diego streets peddling (for a penny) his new paper, and, by the time the day was over, he had sold most of the one thousand copies he had had the printer run. It was a hopeful beginning. When Captain Friend returned to his office and dumped the pile of pennies on his desk, he counted a grand total of eight dollars and fifty-seven cents. But much still had to be done. His weekly paper was due out again on the following Monday, so he had to spend the next few days trying to sell ads and notices, looking for news stories, and getting everything in shape so he could be out on the street again in a week selling the second issue of *The Weekly Drift*.

It wasn't long before Bum found his way to Captain Friend's office, and soon the dog began to spend a good deal of his time accompanying the captain on his rounds. Bum enjoyed the companionship of the new editor as he visited businesses to sell ads and peddled his paper around town. Bum also discovered that Captain Friend's little office was a very comfortable place to sleep.

Late one night, as Captain Friend struggled over a story to be featured on the front page of his paper and Bum lay on the floor next to him, the editor had an idea.

Almost everyone in town knew Bum. But very few people knew much about the pooch except that he had shown up one day, adopted the town, and now followed the newsboys—or Captain Friend—as well as taking on the role of "fire-dog." What was the true story of Bum? Where had he come from and why had he chosen San Diego as his own town? Obviously, Bum was not going to tell him. And there was no one else who might provide information. It was up to the captain and his own imagination to create a believable story of this town dog, his origins, and his adventures.

So he began a series of articles for his newspaper—articles that would occupy a central spot on the front page—detailing the story of this homeless animal and his life and adventures. While much of his story was quite possible, sometimes the inventive writer got a bit carried away in his creation. It didn't matter. Once the stories began to appear, his eager readers couldn't get enough of them. Captain Friend found that Bum and his story gave him exactly what he needed to attract a devoted readership. He even increased his print run to three thousand copies. And the paper still sold out. His readers loved it and so, issue by issue, *The Weekly Drift* featured the continuing story of Bum, and it was a huge success.

This is how his series began:

Bum, the Town Dog

We see him almost every day. Many of us enjoy his company. Many local shop owners are happy to supply the scraps and bones that provide his meals. But who really is this dog who has decided to adopt San Diego as his town?

The Dog that Belonged to No One

He was born July 1, 1885, in the dog pound of that notorious northern city, San Francisco. His mother was a spaniel who had been picked up as a stray just a short time before. His father was probably a St. Bernard.

The pound workers, realizing that she was soon to give birth, allowed Bum's mother to deliver her litter. It consisted of a grand total of six.

Unfortunately, no one claimed the mother and not many animal adoptions were happening during those tough financial times so, sadly, the mother and five of the pups eventually had to be put to sleep. Bum, however, then—as now—proved to be the lucky one.

He was adopted—just a day before he would have met the same fate as the rest of his family—by a local tradesman, and soon he became a fixture at the man's shop.

Bum spent the first four months of his life in the shop, but living such a leisurely life was not part of his nature.

On a bright spring morning in March, he felt a sense of adventure and curiosity bubbling up in him.

So he trotted down to the wharf, carefully slipped aboard the steamer *Santa Rosa* as a stowaway, and, a few days later, disembarked at the dock in San Diego, there to begin a new and exciting life.

His life has been a series of fascinating adventures. In future issues of *The Weekly Drift,* I
will relate some of the more interesting ones to
allow our readers to know more about this dog
we all know and love who is called Bum.

11

The Popularity

As each new story appeared about Bum, the dog's popularity increased. More people now recognized him on the street, more shop owners were eager to provide handouts to this well-known "personality," and crowds of children often followed him.

Stories about Bum (some courtesy of Captain Friend's articles) were told by almost everyone and a few clever folks decided to climb aboard the Bum Bandwagon.

A fashionable restaurant called "Arthur's Place," from which the chef had once or twice supplied Bum with some leftovers, was happy to place a sign in its window. The sign proclaimed (with a bit of exaggeration) "Bum Eats Here!" Whether or not visiting a place known for providing dog scraps was something to attract new patrons, Arthur's Place felt that the sign made the restaurant more popular with local diners.

Other eateries followed suit and soon so many restaurants insisted that Bum took his meals from them, it was a bit hard to believe that any one dog could eat so much so often!

Then a local photography studio decided to take advantage of Bum's popularity. Hubert DeLacey was a photographer who specialized in those stiff and awkward pictures of families and wedding couples. One reason they were usually so stiff was that the people had to remain still for as long as eight minutes. The film plates on which the pictures were taken were much less sensitive to light in those days, so those who wanted a portrait had to hold their pose rigidly in front of the camera without moving.

DeLacey—who just happened to have placed an advertisement in *The Weekly Drift* —stopped Captain Friend on one of the editor's rounds of the neighborhood. Bum was tagging along at the time, and DeLacey asked if the good captain might lend him the dog for a short time as he was having a problem keeping a child still for one of his photos.

Friend consented and soon Bum was in the picture with the youngsters, keeping the little ones interested, and adding to the comfortable composition of the portrait.

When the photo was developed, DeLacey—and the children's parents—were more than delighted. He

PHOTOGRAPHER

Hubert DeLacey

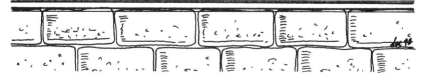

proudly displayed a copy of the photo in his shop window, and, before very long, others wanted Bum included in their family portraits.

Soon Bum began to appear in many photographs that graced the mantlepieces of families all over the city. He had now become Bum, the picture dog!

12

The Hero

On a cold morning in January, 1891, Bum was wandering along the streets of the city. It was a Sunday and the town was quiet. Most folks were in church or, perhaps, sleeping late on this day when the majority were not working.

Captain Friend was asleep and the newsboys had no papers to sell. Bum was left on his own, and, on days like this one, would generally spend his time satisfying his curiosity, exploring the city's nooks and crannies.

On this day he had wandered down to the docks. It was here that he had first arrived in San Diego those many years ago, and it was here his career as "town dog" had begun.

But Bum was not the only one who was exploring the city on this chilly morning.

The Dog that Belonged to No One

Unknown to anyone, Wilbur Michael Standish, who was all of two and a half years of age, had climbed out of his crib that morning and was, at the same moment, toddling down the street. No one in his house was awake and his parents assumed the little one was not able to climb out of his crib—or even open the front door. Little did they know how skillful and persistent a toddler can be.

The Standish home was not more than half a block from the docks and little Wilbur had always loved watching the fishing boats and steamers his mother took him to see.

Now as Bum stood watching the water, little Wilbur also was approaching the dock. But at the age of two and half, the child was hardly as sure-footed as the dog.

Bum was aware of something near him and turned just at the very instant little Wilbur screamed in fright as he lost his footing on the wet wharf and plummeted six feet into the cold waters of San Diego Bay.

The dog saw the splash as the infant hit the water. His reaction was immediate. Without hesitation Bum leaped from the dock into the bay, and in a moment had reached the struggling child. Gently he grabbed the child's nightshirt in his teeth and began to swim to the nearest fishing boat.

Bum and Wilbur were not the only ones who had come to the docks that day. At the same moment the fisherman Ah Woe Sue was crossing "H" Street head-

ing toward his boat to do some repair on his damaged nets. For Ah Woe Sue, even Sunday often was a work day.

As he climbed down to his own boat, he saw the dog struggling with the baby not far away. The fisherman immediately realized what had happened and clambered from boat to boat, reaching dog and child in a matter of minutes. Soon he was pounding the back of the child and using his primitive means of artificial respiration to insure that the water would get out and the air would get in.

Luckily he was successful. Soon Wilbur Michael Standish was screaming in fear and the fisherman and the dog knew he was alive.

The three of them were in the boat: the screaming, soaking, freezing child, the dripping dog, and the fisherman. Ah Woe Sue had pulled off his coat and wrapped it around the shivering infant and was holding Wilbur close to him in an attempt to calm him—as well as warm him.

By this time, the child's parents had discovered him missing and were scouring the neighborhood. Terror-stricken, they searched everywhere for the wandering toddler.

It was Wilbur's mother who reached the dock first and heard the screaming. Soon she was peering down to see the child and his rescuers crouched in the fishing boat.

Ah Woe Sue looked up to where the woman stood.

The Hero

"Baby fall in water. Dog save him."
The woman screamed.

By afternoon the story was all over town. Bum had added to his titles of town dog, fire dog, and picture dog, the most respected of all titles: hero. He had saved a child's life. This story was sure to appear in the next edition of *The Weekly Drift*—as well as every other city paper.

13

The Celebrity

The word spread rapidly about Bum's heroism. When Captain Friend heard of it, he quickly rushed to find out where Ah Woe Sue lived—in the Chinese section of the city—and got as much of the story as the fisherman knew. Then he rushed to the home of the infant who had been saved and tried to interview the Standish family. But he found the father and mother had little to say. After all, he soon realized, they must have been feeling some responsibility for what happened, and they certainly didn't want a reporter making things worse than they already were.

Unfortunately for Captain Friend, it was *The Union* (his former employer) that came out with the story first and *The Drift*—though it presented a more detailed account (with much more praise for Bum's courage)—did not appear until some days later.

The Dog that Belonged to No One

Bum, of course, took the whole thing in stride. However, he did discover that he had suddenly gained a large number of new admirers and food was being brought to him at the office of *The Weekly Drift*. He didn't even have to make the rounds of restaurants and butcher shops anymore.

Another result of the dog's new celebrity status was his coverage in the Captain's weekly paper. Friend had already discovered that Bum's exploits made good copy and helped sell newspapers. He was now selling about three thousand copies per week. So he decided to get even more creative in describing the dog's heroism. He told about the rescue of the little boy in two separate issues. Then he proceeded to tell of numerous other adventures of the now famous dog.

Bum, he wrote, had on a previous occasion rescued a tiny puppy that had wandered out onto the tracks of the horse trolley line. When Bum saw that the vehicle was almost upon the little dog, he had sprung into action, grabbing the pup with his teeth by the scruff of the neck and pulling the tiny dog to safety.

As a fire dog, Friend wrote, he had on one occasion leaped through the smoky window of a house that was engulfed in flames. By his loud barking he had awakened its sleeping occupants and helped them find their way to safety.

At another time, Bum had led a party of searchers trying to locate a lost hiker in rugged terrain. It was the dog, boasted the editor, that had been responsible for finding the lost man—when the search party was just about ready to give up looking.

How true any of these situations might have been and how many of them were invented by a writer who saw Bum's heroism as profitable is open to argument. But they not only sold papers, they also made Bum a living legend. *The Drift* was soon printing over four thousand copies each week—and Captain Friend's faithful newsboys were now assisting him in his paper's distribution and sale.

Local politicians also saw the advantage of having Bum on their side. Mayor Douglas Gunn invited the dog to visit him for a day and made sure the newspapers made note of his generosity.

That fall at election time Bum was invited to lead a torchlight parade on the night before the voters went to the polls. And it was no small coincidence, many said, that the candidate who rode in the parade in which Bum marched was the winner.

The famous canine also made frequent appearances in patriotic parades, leading the brass bands with his familiar three-legged strut.

He would march in funeral processions as well. On these occasions, he walked in a more serious manner, his stump of a tail respectfully lowered behind him.

Perhaps the high point of Bum's celebrity status came in 1891 when the city of San Diego received a visit from the President of the United States, Benjamin Harrison. The chief executive's arrival by train was greeted by a large group of local city officials who assembled as the presidential train arrived. Bum was there too. He stood beside the Mayor as President Harrison stepped off the train, and even rode in a carriage as part of the gala parade that preceded the President through town.

Bum, however, did not get to eat at the official dinner, and had to be content to munch on his bone outside the door of the Presidential banquet.

In truth, this once homeless dog had arrived.

14

The Dogcatcher

While many two-legged creatures had made major contributions to the success, well being, and fame of Bum, another was to have a slightly different effect. This man's name was Lorenzo Hummel.

Lorenzo Hummel had arrived in San Diego some months after Bum's major celebrity status had reached its peak. He did not read Captain Friend's newspaper—he probably didn't read any paper. He lived in a part of town that Bum had very likely never visited, so he knew nothing at all about this famous animal.

Hummel worked for the city in a variety of jobs. But when the assistant city pound master died suddenly, Hummel saw this event as a major opportunity for promotion. He requested—and received—appointment to this job. Lorenzo Hummel became the town dogcatcher.

Shortly after his appointment, the city fathers decided that there were too many stray and unlicensed dogs wandering the city. Hummel was called in to his superior's office and given his instructions: round up all unlicensed dogs.

Now remember Bum had over all the years of his life in San Diego never really belonged to anyone. He had never been licensed and no one who knew him ever felt that this dog required a license. He was above all that petty nonsense.

But Lorenzo Hummel knew nothing about this.

On a warm May day, Hummel was going about his required task of animal roundup when he spotted Bum lying in the street taking an afternoon nap— something the dog frequently did.

Bum was so well known to most people of the town that horses drew their carriages around him and pedestrian traffic parted so Bum would not be disturbed.

But Hummel only knew that here was an unlicensed mongrel lying in the street.

This called for immediate action. He carefully approached the dog with a strong wire collar and his net. Deftly Hummel looped the device around Bum's neck, and, when the startled animal awoke, he found himself being wrestled to the waiting dogcatcher's wagon.

The Dog that Belonged to No One

Although Lorenzo Hummel had no idea who Bum was, several young men lounging outside Fenster's Hardware Store knew the dog well. When they saw the famous dog being viciously treated by this ignorant public servant, they rushed to his rescue.

Before Hummel had reached the wagon, he found himself surrounded by a group of angry young citizens. When he refused to free the dog, citing his official orders to pick up strays, he began to be pushed, pulled, and beaten by the young men who encircled him. Bum, who had now broken free, watched cooly as the poor dogcatcher was manhandled by the rowdy group and left lying in the middle of the street.

Poor Lorenzo Hummel limped his way back to the pound and reported his rude treatment by the angry citizens. His account soon reached the office of Mayor Gunn himself. The Mayor realized who the dog was but he also realized that official orders had to be followed and public officials could not be treated so savagely.

The Mayor called a meeting of all the town officials. How should they handle a crisis of this magnitude?

"Fire the deputy pound master," insisted one.

"Arrest those who attacked the man," argued another.

"Stop catching strays," suggested a sensitive soul.

The Dogcatcher

"Wait," shouted an intelligent voice. "There's a simple solution."

The city fathers turned expectantly to the one who had spoken.

"Let's just give Bum an honorary dog license."

It was too simple.

In a moment there was total agreement.

"Of course," said the Mayor, "he *is* the town dog."

"And something else," continued the same voice of reason.

Again they all turned to him.

"Since Bum is the town dog, I think his picture should be put on all dog licenses."

There was another moment of silence and then the room erupted in cheers.

Thus in a ceremony in Mayor Gunn's office (but with Lorenzo Hummel unfortunately absent), Bum was presented with honorary license number 587. The license was bestowed on him for life, and it, like all licenses issued from that time on, bore the picture of Bum, the official town dog.

Bum, of course, accepted the license, and the additional notoriety in his usual cool and disinterested way. In the eyes of many he may have become a celebrity, but he was still just a dog.

15

The Anniversary

The year 1892 was an important occasion for the city of San Diego. It had been just 350 years since explorer Juan Rodriquez Cabrillo had discovered the port during the course of his explorations. On September 28, 1542, Cabrillo and his crew sailed into San Diego Bay, the first Spanish expedition to reach the California coast.

The city fathers discussed the idea of marking this occasion with a major celebration.

Plans were suggested for a parade and band concert as well as a lavish three day festival on September 28, 29, and 30, to commemorate the discovery of what had become the city of San Diego.

Unfortunately this was not a good time financially for the city. The real estate boom had collapsed and many people had left the city because land was not selling and business was bad. Banks had closed and many investors had lost a good deal of money. Some were predicting that there might be a major depression.

In spite of the bad business climate, Billy Carlson, a real estate salesman and eager promoter of the city, pushed hard for the celebration. (Carlson would become the Mayor not long after this.) He promoted the idea even though money was scarce.

Carlson had argued that it would be good to have a major event like this since it might bring people into town. After a lengthy debate, the city fathers agreed that it was an important occasion to recognize despite the bad business climate and decided to allocate $5000 for the grand event.

So plans went ahead for the big celebration.

The day was to begin with a dramatic re-creation of the landing of Juan Cabrillo.

Naturally Captain Friend representing his paper was on hand and Bum, who generally showed up at most official city events was also present along with several hundred others.

Everyone had gathered at the foot of "D" Street to welcome the small ship that was representing Cabrillo's *San Salvador*. The part of Cabrillo was to be enacted by a fisherman from La Playa whose name was Juan Cabral. The fisherman had been given a costume to represent Cabrillo complete with knee-pants, a velvet jacket, and an ostrich plume elegantly extending from his hat.

The plan was for the boat to arrive when the tide was in so that it could sail right up to the wooden wharf at the foot of "D" Street and Cabral would officially take possession of the land in the name of the King of Spain, as Cabrillo had done 350 years before.

But the best laid plans often encounter problems. Cabral's boat got lost sailing along the coast and when he finally sighted the spot where he was supposed to land, the tide had already gone out. His boat ended up stuck in the mud several hundred feet from shore. Cabral dutifully climbed out and hiked through the mud to the waiting throng.

By now several hundred citizens had flocked to the little wooden pier to see the landing. Unfortunately the pier was not a very stable structure—and had not been designed to have so many people crowded on it.

Just as "Cabrillo" was about to plant the Spanish flag, the rickety wharf gave way and a host of assembled dignitaries—including the mayor, several members of the City Council and their wives, as well as Bum—fell into the bay. Of course, with the tide out, the assembled dignitaries ended up splashing in ankle deep mud. Luckily no one was hurt.

Bum probably enjoyed the experience most of all as he cavorted about on his three legs, barking and shaking mud over everyone who was anywhere near him.

The Anniversary

In spite of this unexpected beginning, the entire assembly—many of them much dirtier than they had expected—joined in a parade up "D" Street to the town plaza. The group was joined by bands from the Army and Marines as well as a lively group from Mexico City playing spirited Spanish music.

The festivities went on for three days, with band music, dancing, and even an exhibit by local Indians from San Luis Rey. They put on a colorful show of Native American dancing and demonstrated their skills at making crafts.

It was a grand three days for all, but unfortunately in the weeks and months that followed, life would change for many residents of San Diego as jobs became scarce, shops went out of business, and many were forced to leave town as they searched for employment.

16

The Candidate

O ne evening as Bum lay quietly in the corner of
Captain Friend's little office, the Captain was
busily at work getting his paper ready for the
printer—or as newspaper people say, "putting the
paper to bed." As he worked, the man suddenly had
an idea.

In the months he had been running his newspaper,
he had gained a good deal of popularity among the
citizens of San Diego. People knew him and knew
Bum. He often spoke to many of those who regularly
bought the paper and had developed many friend-
ships.

But things were changing and there was a feeling
among many people that the future of the city did not
look good.

Captain Friend knew that there would be an election for mayor later that year, and he believed that if anyone might be a good candidate, he certainly would be.

He had his paper to promote his ideas and explain the goals he could propose if elected. He knew plenty of people. And he felt sure he could be an excellent mayor if he was elected.

The next day the captain spent some time at City Hall discovering what he had to do to become an official candidate for office. He learned that he had to get a petition signed by 1000 citizens of the city to qualify for the ballot.

So he secured the proper petitions, filled them out, and spent the rest of the afternoon seeking the needed signatures. Bum followed him happily as he went from shop to shop and door to door explaining what he was doing.

Those who knew Captain Friend were happy to hear some of his ideas for the future of the city. They eagerly signed his petition and agreed that he might well make a good candidate for mayor of the city.

It didn't hurt to have Bum along since many people who didn't know the captain had heard of Bum and his exploits. Though Bum didn't know it, he proved to be an excellent campaign assistant.

It took the captain just four days to get the names he needed for his official petitions.

When he and Bum headed back to City Hall, he had a stack of petitions with a total of 1098 names.

The Candidate

Captain James E. Friend would see his name on the official ballot as a candidate for mayor of the city of San Diego. It was an exciting moment. Now he just needed to convince another thousand people (or more) that he was the right man for the job so they would vote for him on election day.

Each week as election day approached, Captain Friend ran regular articles in *The Weekly Drift* stating his thoughts about the city and his ideas for changes that he believed would benefit the people.

He felt there should be more parks. He wanted to make the city more attractive to new businesses. He wanted to have electricity extended all the way to the outskirts of the city.

Many people agreed with his ideas. But what the captain was not noticing was that many things in the city were changing. In just a few months eight stores had closed for lack of business. Jobs were becoming hard to get, and the number of people leaving the city had become greater than the number arriving.

The other candidates were speaking about these things, but the captain often missed them in his eagerness to promote his new ideas.

Election day arrived and, after the captain cast his ballot early in the morning, Bum and Captain Friend spent much of the day at the polling place.

When the polls closed, the captain watched as the box of ballots was put on a wagon and taken to City Hall for the official count.

The Dog that Belonged to No One

Later in the day the Captain and Bum joined a crowd of citizens gathered at City Hall waiting expectantly for the results.

Finally the clerk came out of the building and on a large blackboard wrote the figures.

Four thousand one hundred votes had been cast.

James E. Friend had received just 98!

Captain Friend couldn't believe it. Almost all those who had signed his petitions (more than a thousand people) had voted for someone else. He thought they had liked his ideas and had honestly felt he would make a good mayor.

As he sadly trudged back to his office with Bum following, his sadness turned to anger.

He reached his office and sat down at his desk.

He was still a writer, and here was a good idea for a story. He began to type out the pages of what would become his little book. He changed all the names and added some funny characters. When he finished, his book would be called *One Thousand Liars*. It would be the story of his campaign for mayor and how it had been created with high hopes and ended up as a disaster.

So while his campaign for mayor did not result in success in political office, it did produce a book by Captain James E. Friend.

17

The Hard Times

Things had gotten very bad for Captain Friend—
as well as many other citizens of San Diego.
More shops and businesses had closed and many
people were out of work. A large number of San Diegans had decided to leave the city and search for
work and better conditions northward in Los Angeles—or almost anyplace where there might be a job.

With money scarce, people were not even willing
to spend a penny for *The Weekly Drift.*

As the number of his readers diminished and
fewer and fewer advertisers were interested in buy-
ing space, Captain Friend realized that the future of
his newspaper was grim. He tried desperately to
keep it going, but the printer's bills and the rent on
his office had to be paid. He also needed to make

enough money for his own survival—even though he lived very modestly.

On a morning late in 1893, Capain Friend rose early, dressed himself in the one suit he had—even though it had become very threadbare, and headed for the office of the *San Diego Union,* the newspaper where he had started his San Diego journalistic career those many years before.

Many of those who had worked there when he started were gone, but editor Halliwell Munson was still there.

Munson was a large, red-faced man with a bald head and a bushy beard that was going gray. He could usually be found sitting at his desk in his shirtsleeves, his dark brown suit jacket hanging behind him on the wooden swivel chair where he sat. Munson worked his reporters hard, but he was a fair man and those who knew him well knew he could be understanding.

The editor eagerly welcomed Captain Friend into his office. He guessed why his former reporter had come and was not surprised when Friend explained that *The Weekly Drift* was about to close down.

"Running a newspaper is tough," said Munson. "Why, even the *Union* is having problems these days. Some major advertisers have gone out of business and people don't want to spend money on papers when every penny is hard to get."

"You know I'm a good reporter," Captain Friend

quickly suggested. "I built *The Drift* from almost nothing and we had a few good years."

"I agree. You certainly did that. I think you had a bit of assistance from that dog of yours, though. Even I enjoyed the stories you did about him."

Munson scratched his beard and thought for a minute.

"Hmm. If I give you a job here, would you continue your stories about Bum?"

"Certainly," responded Captain Friend quickly.

"Well, I'm willing to try it," said Munson. He quickly added, "I can only give you a part time job now. But maybe we can move you to a full time position—if things improve."

Captain Friend shook his hand eagerly and thanked him several times before he left.

Once again it seemed that Bum had helped save the day.

It was late in the afternoon when Captain Friend—followed by Bum—began the task of cleaning up the office of *The Weekly Drift.*

Sadly, the Captain disposed of his files and old newspapers. He cleaned out his desk drawers and swept the floor. On the next day the used furniture man would arrive with his horse and wagon to pick up the desks and chairs which the Captain would sell for a few dollars.

One item he would keep was the old typewriter along with a few personal items from the office. The

Captain hoisted the typewriter on his shoulder and headed back to the boarding house where he had lived all these years.

He turned and looked back at the little office. Many months ago he had placed a small sign in the window that proclaimed, *"The Weekly Drift,* San Diego's finest newspaper."

There were tears in his eyes as he walked away. His experiment had been a small success. But now he would return to the reporter's life. No longer an editor and publisher, he had made another major change, but, as always, he moved off with hope. Bum, however, unaware that things had changed, limped along behind him.

18

The Last Years

As a reporter for *The Union*, Captain Friend continued his articles about Bum, as well as many
other tales of residents of San Diego who were
doing—or had done—interesting things.

His columns were popular with almost everyone.
They were a welcome relief from the paper's numerous stories of crime, politics, and the many woes people were suffering during these hard times.

He wrote several articles about the newsboys, who
had become his friends over the years. Those he had
known when he first came to the city were now
grown with families of their own, but he still invited
them to his regular weekly outings in the park—
along with the youngsters who now delivered *The
Union*.

When the family of one of the newsboys had problems—a father out of work or a mother with a severe illness—he would organize collections of food to help the family survive.

Captain Friend still made his rounds of the city, looking for stories of unusual people or interesting situations.

He had met Ah Woe Sue when the little toddler had fallen into the bay and the Captain decided to interview the fisherman again to find out more about his life—as well as the lives of many of the Chinese residents of the city.

He wrote about how ordinary people were surviving the tough times by selling what they made or growing vegetables in their back yards or raising ducks and chickens.

He wrote several columns about the Coronado Hotel, now a grand structure that attracted wealthy visitors from all over the world.

He wrote about the tent city that had grown up around the hotel as a popular spot for ordinary citizens who wanted to spend their summer vacations on the island, enjoy the seashore, and bask in the sun.

Captain Friend's articles became popular with San Diego residents and he became a respected reporter whose work was eagerly read by young and old, rich and poor.

But his old infirmities were beginning to bother him. He was only in his fifties but rheumatism made it harder for him to get around the city and he was plagued by constant shortness of breath.

Bum still kept him company on his rounds, when the captain was able to make them, and the dog would still occasionally follow the young newsboys, and even—now and then—follow the fire wagon.

But Bum too was aging and did not have the enthusiasm to go dashing off to every fire the way he had just a few years before.

On a Monday morning in March, 1898, Mrs. Williardson, the landlady of the boarding house at 1054 Seventh Street where Captain Friend had lived for the last two years, was surprised when the Captain did not make his appearance at the breakfast table. He was usually prompt, had his coffee and toast, then headed off for the newspaper office right on schedule.

She climbed the stairs and tapped on the door of his room, but there was no response. She knocked even louder, but there was still no response. Alarmed, Mrs. Williardson opened the door (the Captain never locked it). She gasped. The Captain lay in bed, his face flushed. She quickly realized he was not breathing. He had died peacefully in his sleep.

Captain Friend had died with no money, but the newsboys—those he had helped all through his life— responded to the call. They went door to door to ask for contributions for a funeral, and all who had known him or read his columns eagerly contributed to the cause. They raised a substantial sum and when the funeral was held, more than three hundred people attended. Many who were there were newsboys who remembered him from the old days and there were many who had worked with him on *The Union*.

Ah Woe Sue was there as were many from the Chinese community of the city.

The City Guard Band was also there to provide appropriate music for the funeral.

Later the mourners gathered at the Mt. Hope Cemetery. Bum was present as well. He was old and had difficulty moving about now, but the dog watched sadly as the Captain was lowered into his grave. If dogs could cry, Bum might well have joined so many others whose tears flowed as they watched Captain Friend's casket get placed in its final resting place.

The newsboys' collection had provided for the funeral and a small tombstone. It said, simply,

James Edward Friend
1840–1898
"the newsboys' friend"

After the Captain's death, the City Council decided that Bum should be retired from his official status as town dog. He spent more time sleeping in the sun now and was too bothered by rheumatism even to show up at city celebrations.

The Dog that Belonged to No One

At the county hospital in Mission Valley, Bum was given the official job of being a guard dog. Here he was well taken care of by the patients and staff, and fed regularly, though he ate very little these days.

But just eight months after the Captain's death, in November of 1898, one of the patients who was taking a walk found the body of Bum under a stairwell. Like the Captain, the dog had died peacefully in his sleep.

People from all over the city contributed to Bum's funeral, and even the children collected pennies for a fitting tribute to the dog who had meant so much to all of them.

Hundreds turned out for the funeral of San Diego's city dog.

The newspapers published many tributes to this famous animal, including these words in the *San Diego Evening Tribune* :

The death of Bum, that good old dog, will be regretted by all public spirited citizens. His was a more active and useful life than nine-tenths of his race.

No one knows exactly where the grave of Bum is. Some think he was buried in Mission Valley not far from the hospital. Others suspect that maybe (though it was not officially permitted) Bum's remains had been placed alongside those of Captain Friend in the Mt. Hope cemetery in San Diego. If it is true, then it is only proper since Bum always managed to do things that would never have been permitted to any other dog.

Many tributes were printed in *The Union* about both the Captain and Bum. But perhaps the most appropriate one came from a longtime resident of San Diego. She wrote:

Bum is more than a memory; he is a symbol of
San Diego. He stands for much that we need today—
loyalty, faithfulness, and devotion.

And Bum might have enjoyed that too. Especially if it had been accompanied by some scratching behind the ears and a nice meat bone.

The End

About the Author

Gerald A. Schiller combined careers as a teacher and film maker for many years. He wrote and directed a number of award-winning educational and documentary films, many of which continue to be shown on television worldwide.

He started writing when he was very young and for many years wrote film scripts for promotional, industrial, and training films as well as feature film scripts and documentaries.

He has won awards from the American Film Festival, Columbus Film Festival, Golden Gate Film Festival and C.I.N.E. (the Council on International Nontheatrical Events).

Deadly Dreams, his first novel, was published recently. His second mystery, *Death Underground*, will be available soon.

His articles and reviews have appeared in publications that include *The Los Angeles Times, Ventura Star, Sightlines, Film News, Mystery Readers Journal,* and *Multimedia News.*

While doing research for articles on early California history, Mr. Schiller came across the story of Bum. Intrigued by the dog's history, he found out all he could about Bum and the result is *The Dog That Belonged to No One.*

Mr. Schiller has two grown children and lives with his wife in Southern California.

About the Artist

Dawn Schiller received her education in design at Illinois Central College, and has gone on to achieve numerous successes in the field of illustration and computer graphics.

Among her many recent accomplishments are exhibit and educational illustrations for the Los Angeles County Museum of Natural History, cover art for the novel *Deadly Dreams*, and numerous comic book illustrations.

She has also worked in the advertising business for many years doing design and illustration.

Dawn is the wife of Gerald Schiller's son, Greg.